D1642509

HO HO HO

santa's christmas

Joke Book

Ho Ho Ho! Santa's Christmas Joke Book

Published by IOM Press in 2018.
www.iompress.org

Copyright © 2018 IOM Press

ISBN : 978-1-9164076-1-9

Contents

Jolly
Holly Day
Jokes

What do you get if you cross a dinosaur with a Christmas tree?

Tree Rex

What did the stamp say to the Christmas card?

Stick with me and we'll go places

What's the best thing to give your parents for Christmas?

A list of everything you want!

Knock, knock!

Who's there?

Justin

Justin who?

Justin time to hear my Christmas jokes!

Why does the Christmas alphabet only have 25 letters in it?

Because there's No-el

What do elves do after
school?

Their gnome work!

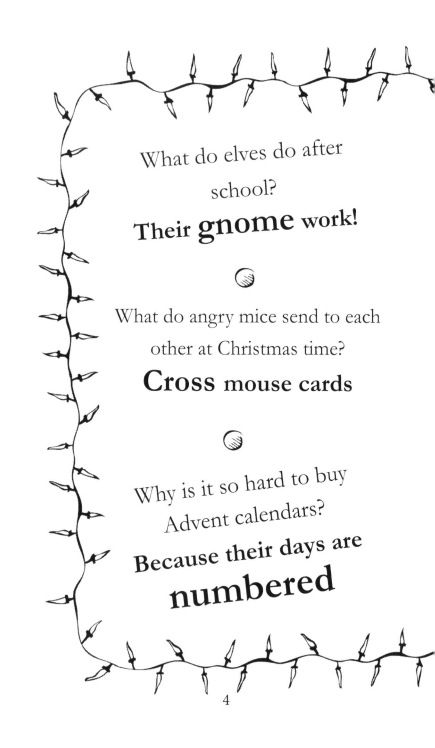

What do angry mice send to each
other at Christmas time?

Cross mouse cards

What do elves do after

Why is it so hard to buy
Advent calendars?

**Because their days are
numbered**

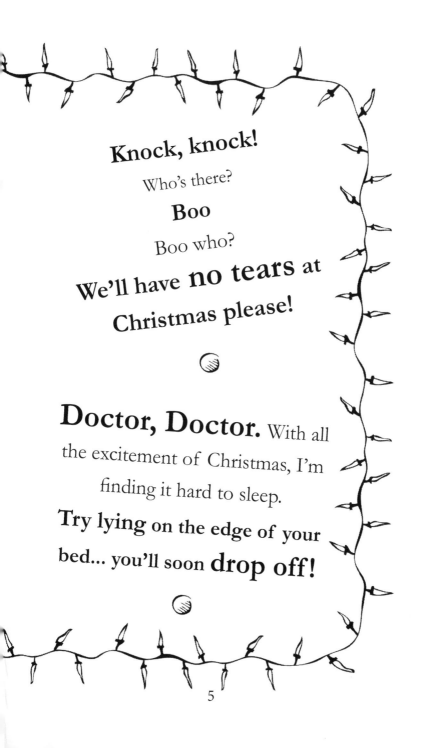

Knock, knock!

Who's there?

Boo

Boo who?

We'll have no tears at Christmas please!

Doctor, Doctor. With all the excitement of Christmas, I'm finding it hard to sleep.

Try lying on the edge of your bed... you'll soon drop off!

Knock, knock!
Who's there?
Holly
Holly who?
Holly-days are here again!

What did one Christmas
angel say to the other?
Halo there!

What's the noisiest part of
a Christmas tree?
Its bark!

Why couldn't the butterfly go to
the Christmas party?
It was a moth ball

What did the spider request
for Christmas?
**A computer so he could
find the best web-sites**

Where do elves go
when they're sick?
**To the elf
centre!**

How did the chickens dance at the Christmas party?
Chick-to-chick!

Who is the elves' favourite singer?
Elf-is Presley

What did the beaver say to the Christmas tree?
It's been nice gnawing you!

Knock, knock!

Who's there?

Coal

Coal who?

Coal me if you hear
Santa coming!

What do you have in December
that you don't have in any other
months?

The letter D

Knock, knock!

Who's there?

Mary and Abby

Mary and Abby who?

Mary Christmas
and **Abby** New Year!

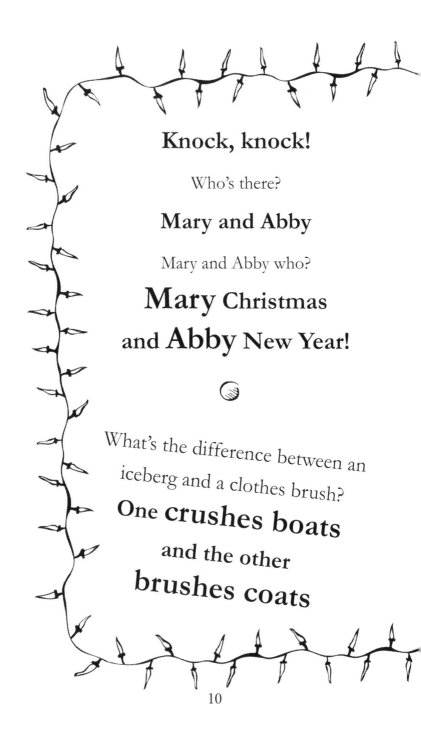

What's the difference between an
iceberg and a clothes brush?

One **crushes boats**
and the other
brushes coats

What do you get if you cross an apple with a Christmas tree?
A pine-apple

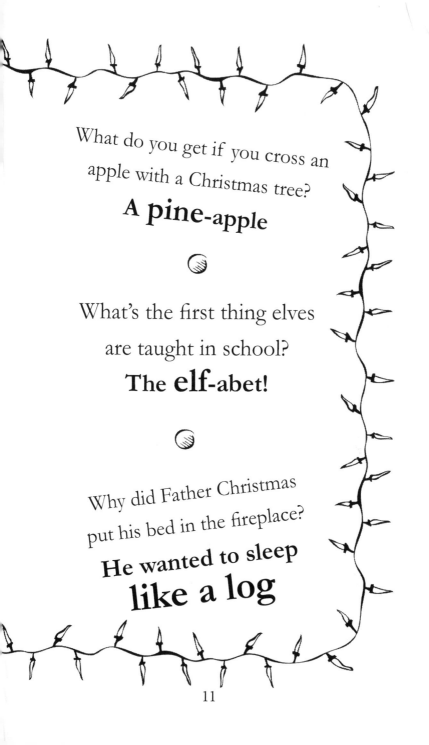

What's the first thing elves are taught in school?
The elf-abet!

Why did Father Christmas put his bed in the fireplace?
He wanted to sleep like a log

Why are Christmas trees
so bad at sewing?
**They are always dropping
their needles**

What did the Christmas stocking

say when it found a hole in itself?

**"Well I'll be
darned"**

What insect doesn't
like Christmas?
A humbug

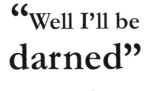

12

Knock, knock!

Who's there?

Squeamish

Squeamish who?

Squeamish you a
Merry Christmas,
Squeamish you a
Merry Christmas,
Squeamish you a
Merry Christmas,
and a Happy
New Year!

What do you call an elf who
has won the lottery?

Welfy!

What's a ghost's favourite Christmas entertainment?

The Phanto-mime!

How do sheep greet each other at Christmas?

Merry Christmas to Ewe

What type of photographs do elves like taking?

Elfies, of course!

Knock, knock!

Who's there?

Police

Police who?

Police don't make me eat Brussels Sprouts this year!

What did the bald man say when he was given a comb for Christmas?

Thanks, I'll never part with it!

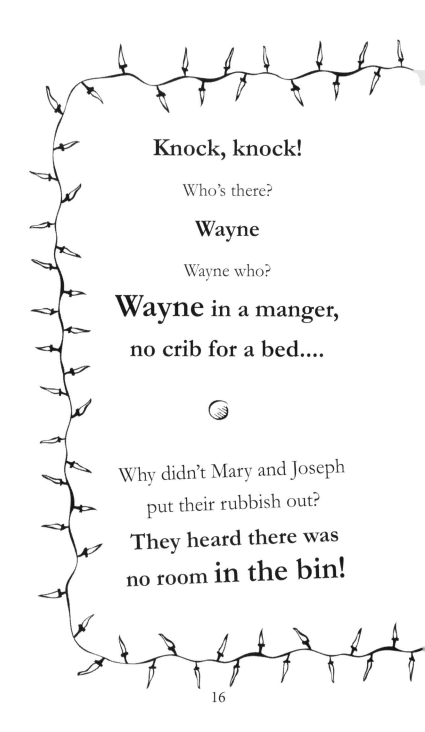

Knock, knock!

Who's there?

Wayne

Wayne who?

Wayne in a manger,
no crib for a bed....

Why didn't Mary and Joseph
put their rubbish out?
**They heard there was
no room in the bin!**

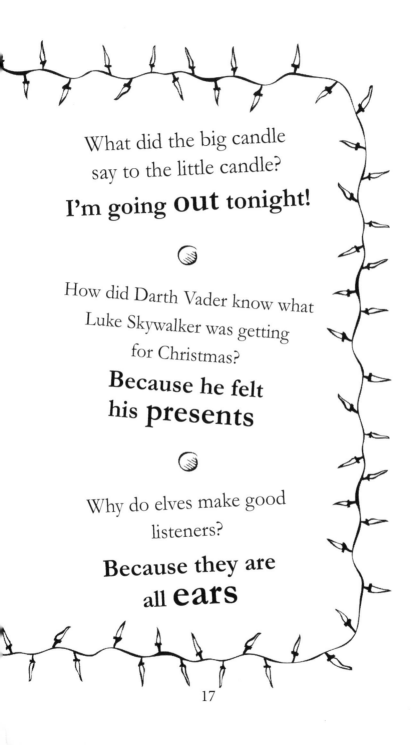

What did the big candle
say to the little candle?

I'm going out tonight!

How did Darth Vader know what
Luke Skywalker was getting
for Christmas?

**Because he felt
his presents**

Why do elves make good
listeners?

**Because they are
all ears**

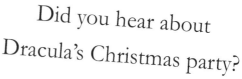

Did you hear about Dracula's Christmas party?

It was a scream

Knock, knock!

Who's there?

Gladys

Gladys who?

Gladys not me

getting

coal this

Christmas

18

What did the smelly stocking say

to the other smelly stocking?

Are you stinking

what I'm stinking?

What did Adam say

the day before Christmas?

"It's Christmas, Eve."

What do you call a sheep

who doesn't

like Christmas?

Baaaa Humbug!

Why didn't the skeleton go to the Christmas party?

Because he had no-body to go with

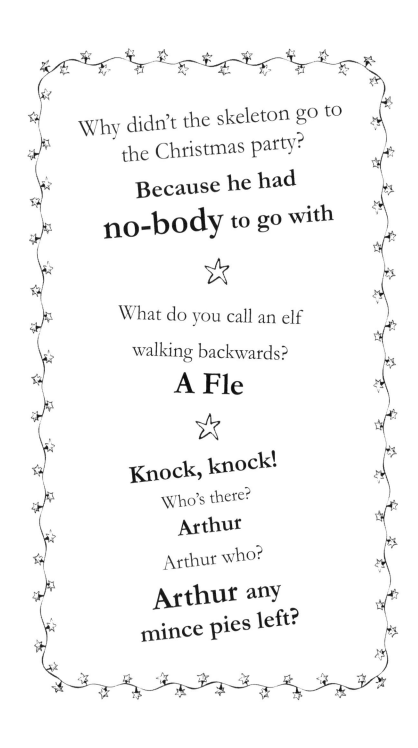

What do you call an elf

walking backwards?

A Fle

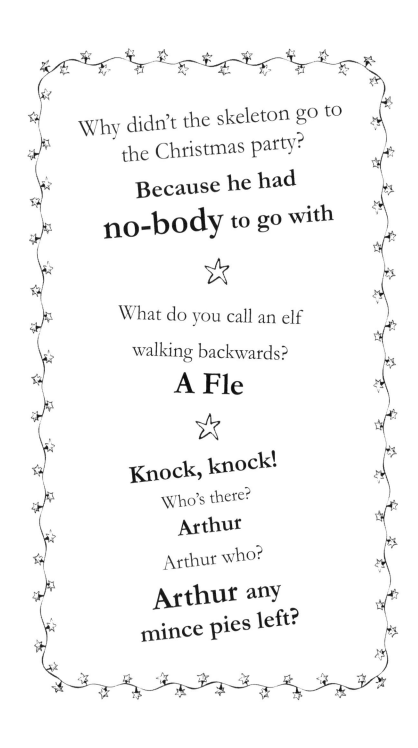

Knock, knock!

Who's there?

Arthur

Arthur who?

Arthur any mince pies left?

Fab-yule-ous One-liners

Are Santa's elves just a bunch of **subordinate Clauses?**

Did you hear that Santa's not allowed to go down any chimneys this year? It was declared unsafe by the **Elf and Safety** Commission.

I was planning to watch *The Art of Present Wrapping* on TV. But then I discovered it was only on **Paper View.**

I've bought my mum a **fridge** for Christmas. I can't wait to see her face **light up** when she opens it.

Did you hear about the chef who was **arrested** while making a Christmas cake? **He was caught beating** the eggs and **whipping** the cream.

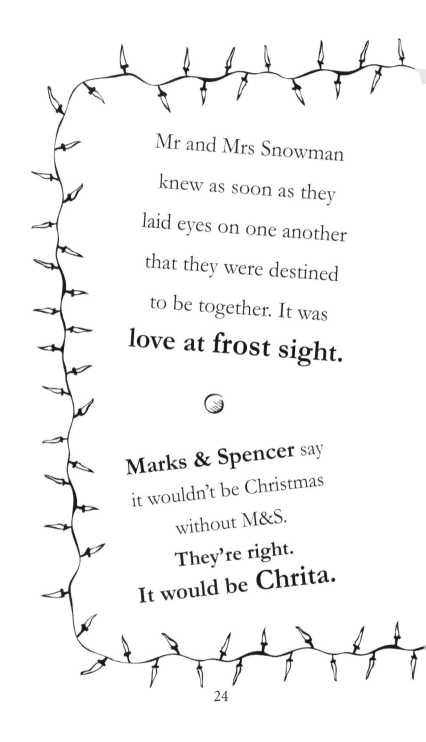

Mr and Mrs Snowman
knew as soon as they
laid eyes on one another
that they were destined
to be together. It was
love at frost sight.

Marks & Spencer say
it wouldn't be Christmas
without M&S.
They're right.
It would be **Chrita.**

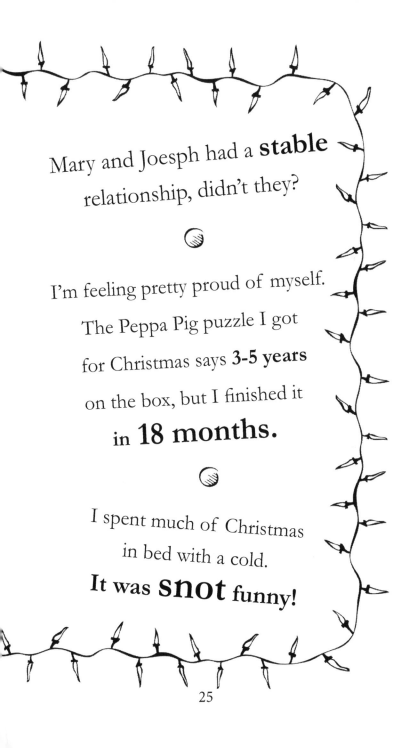

Mary and Joesph had a **stable** relationship, didn't they?

I'm feeling pretty proud of myself. The Peppa Pig puzzle I got for Christmas says **3-5 years** on the box, but I finished it **in 18 months.**

I spent much of Christmas in bed with a cold. **It was snot funny!**

My grandmother has been **staring through the window** ever since it started to snow. If it gets any worse, I'll have to **let her in.**

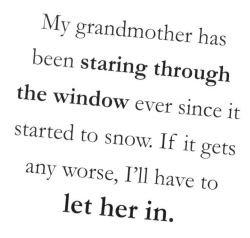

Did you hear about the **kidnapping** during Midnight Mass? Fortunately, he woke up.

26

My friend Sam got a **wooden leg** for Christmas. It wasn't his main present, it was just a **stocking filler.**

The best Christmas present I ever got was a broken drum.

You simply can't beat it.

When Santa's in your room, can you sense his **presents?**

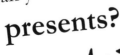

My dad once bought me a pack of batteries for Christmas, with a note saying **"Toys not included"**.

☆

I used to work in an **Advent calendar** factory... but I quit after my boss said I couldn't **take a day off.**

☆

I got a new pair of gloves for Christmas, but they're **both 'lefts'...**
which on the one hand is great, but on the other, **just doesn't feel right.**

Which of Santa's reindeer has the worst manners?

Rude-olph

Why didn't Rudolph go to school?

He was elf-taught

How do you get into Rudolph's house?

By ringing the deer-bell

Knock, knock!

Who's there?

Olive

Olive who?

Olive the other reindeer

What do you call a reindeer
in the Sahara Desert?

Lost!

What do you call a reindeer with three eyes?

Reiiindeer

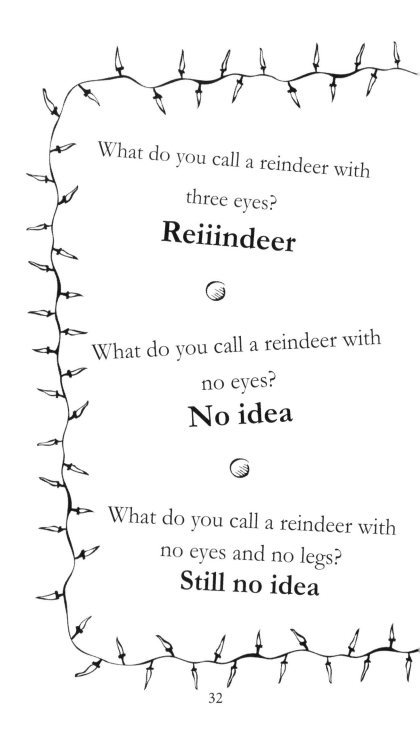

What do you call a reindeer with no eyes?

No idea

What do you call a reindeer with no eyes and no legs?

Still no idea

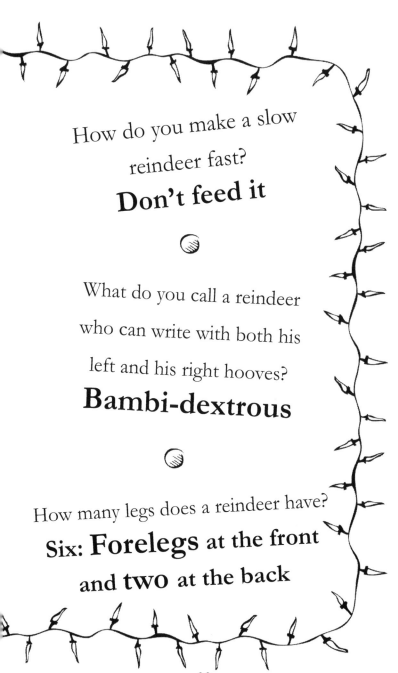

How do you make a slow
reindeer fast?
Don't feed it

What do you call a reindeer
who can write with both his
left and his right hooves?
Bambi-dextrous

How many legs does a reindeer have?
Six: **Forelegs** at the front
and **two** at the back

What do
reindeer hang on their
Christmas trees?
Hornaments

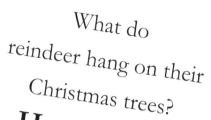

What do you call a reindeer
wearing earmuffs?
**Anything
you like,
as he won't be
able to
hear you!**

Which reindeer can jump higher

than a house?

**They all can - houses
can't jump!**

Why did no-one bid for

Rudolph and Prancer on eBay?

**Because they were
two deer**

If a reindeer lost his tail,

where would he

go to buy a new one?

To a retail shop!

35

What do you call a
three-legged reindeer?
Eileen

What do you give a reindeer
with an upset stomach?
An **Elk-aseltzer**

Why do reindeer have fur coats?
**Because they'd
look silly in
anoraks!**

What do reindeer have that other animals don't have?
Baby reindeer

Why is Rudolph so good at answering trivia questions?
Because he nose a lot and is very bright.

Why does Santa always ask
Dasher and Dancer to fetch him
his coffee?

**Because they are
his star bucks**

☆

What does Rudolph want
for Christmas?

A Pony Sleigh Station

☆

What's the difference between a
biscuit and a reindeer?

**You can't dunk a
reindeer in your tea!**

Silly Santa Jokes

Who delivers Christmas
presents to dogs?
Santa Paws

What goes Ho Ho Whoosh?
**Santa going through
a revolving door**

Why did the traffic warden give
Santa a parking ticket?
**He left his sleigh in the
Snow Parking Zone**

What's red and white
and goes up and down,
up and down?

**Santa
on a trampoline**

What is 12 metres long,
6 metres tall, has sharp teeth and
goes 'Ho Ho Ho'?

Tyranno-santa-rex

What did Santa say to Mrs Claus
when he looked out of the window
on Christmas Eve?

It looks like rain, dear.

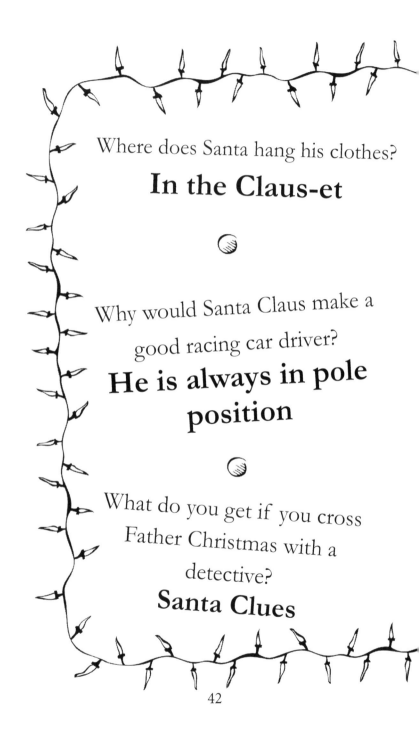

Where does Santa hang his clothes?

In the Claus-et

Why would Santa Claus make a good racing car driver?

He is always in pole position

What do you get if you cross Father Christmas with a detective?

Santa Clues

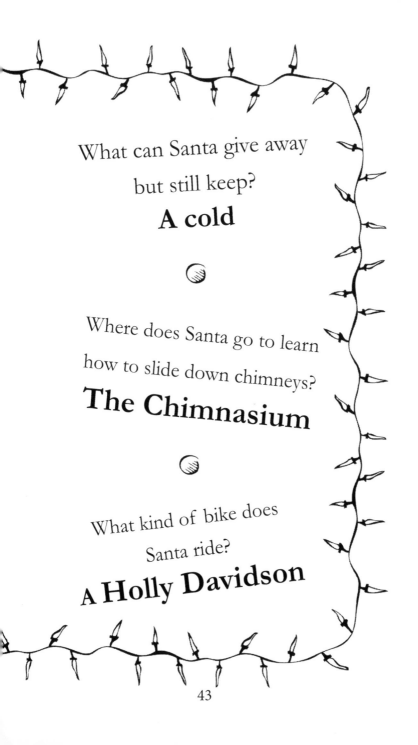

What can Santa give away
but still keep?

A cold

Where does Santa go to learn
how to slide down chimneys?

The Chimnasium

What kind of bike does
Santa ride?

A Holly Davidson

What do you call people
who are afraid of Santa Claus?

Claus-trophobic

Knock, knock!

Who's there?

Alaska

Alaska who?

Alaska Santa for
a new bike
for Christmas

44

What did the banana say to Santa
when he came down the chimney?

**Nothing, bananas
don't talk!**

Where does Santa

keep his money?

In a snow bank

What do you call a cat on

the beach at Christmas?

Sandy Claws!

45

What do you get if you cross Santa with a duck?

A Christmas Quacker

Why does Santa like using chimneys to deliver all his presents?

Because it soots him

What did the iceberg sing to Father Christmas on his birthday?

"Freeze a jolly good fellow..."

Knock, knock!

Who's there?

Ho Ho

Ho Ho who?

Your Santa impression needs a little work!

Why don't you ever see Father Christmas in hospital?

Because he has private elf care

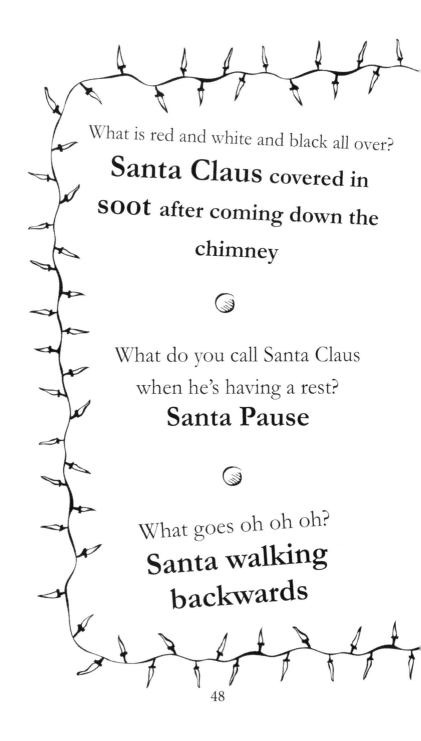

What is red and white and black all over?
Santa Claus covered in
soot after coming down the
chimney

What do you call Santa Claus
when he's having a rest?
Santa Pause

What goes oh oh oh?
**Santa walking
backwards**

What do you call a man who claps at Christmas?

Santapplause

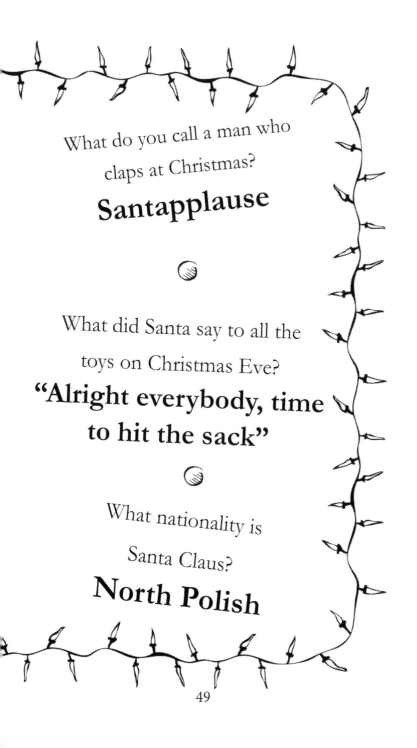

What did Santa say to all the toys on Christmas Eve?

"Alright everybody, time to hit the sack"

What nationality is Santa Claus?

North Polish

What goes red, white, red, white, red, white...?

Santa rolling down a hill

Where does Santa stay when he goes on holiday?

In a ho-ho-hotel

What did the elves call Santa when he lost his pants?

Saint Knickerless!

How does Batman's mother call him for Christmas dinner?

Dinner, dinner, dinner, dinner, dinner, dinner, dinner, dinner, Batman!

Child: Mum, can I have a dog for Christmas?

Mother: No, you can have turkey like everyone else!

Why should you never set the turkey next to the dessert?

Because he will gobble gobble it up!

What did the gelatine say at Christmas?

'Tis the season to be jelly

If fruit comes from a fruit tree, where does turkey come from?

A Poul-tree!

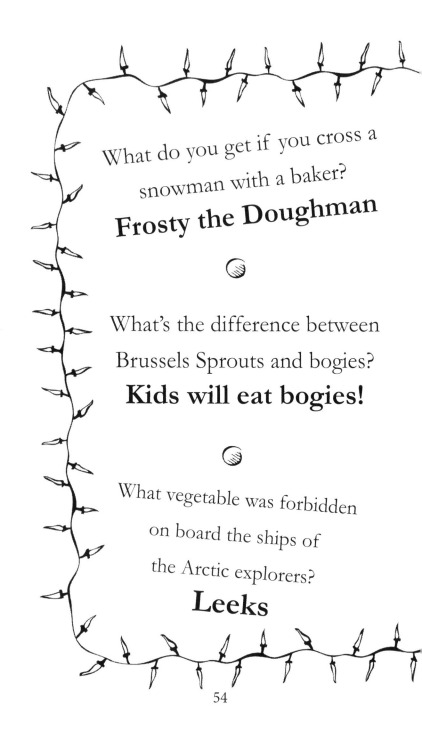

What do you get if you cross a
snowman with a baker?
Frosty the Doughman

What's the difference between
Brussels Sprouts and bogies?
Kids will eat bogies!

What vegetable was forbidden
on board the ships of
the Arctic explorers?
Leeks

What's a snowman's favourite
supermarket?

Iceland

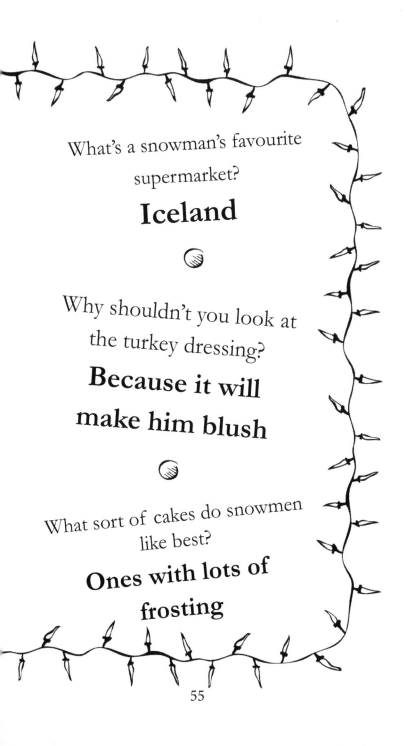

Why shouldn't you look at
the turkey dressing?

**Because it will
make him blush**

What sort of cakes do snowmen
like best?

**Ones with lots of
frosting**

Who is never hungry
on Christmas Day?
The turkey,
because
he is always
stuffed

Who did one snowman
say to the other?
**Can you smell
carrots?**

Why did the turkey cross the road?

He was pretending to be a chicken!

What did the elf say to Santa when teaching him to use the Chrismas computer?

"First YULE LOG-on"

What do you call a lobster who won't share any of his Christmas presents?

Shellfish

What's the key to a good Christmas?

The tur-key!

What's a mathematician's favourite Christmas snack?

Mince-pi

Why did the gingerbread man go to the doctor?

He was feeling crummy

What did the
snowman order
at McDonald's?

**An iceberger with
extra chilly sauce!**

What happened when the turkey
got into a fight?

**He had the stuffing
knocked out
of him**

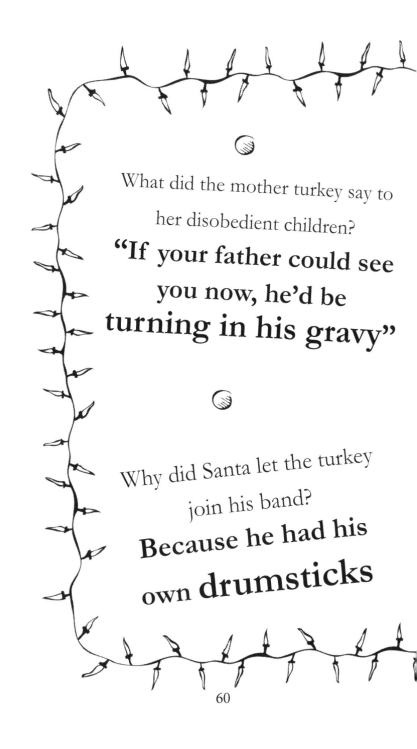

What did the mother turkey say to
her disobedient children?

**"If your father could see
you now, he'd be
turning in his gravy"**

Why did Santa let the turkey
join his band?

**Because he had his
own drumsticks**

What kind of bread do elves
like best?

Shortbread!

What would you get if you
crossed a turkey with a ghost?

A poultry-geist

Who beats his chest and swings
from Christmas cake to
Christmas cake?

Tarzipan!

Why did Santa's little helpers choose the outside table at the restaurant?

They wanted to eat elfresco

Why did the police arrest the turkey?

They suspected it of fowl play

What's white, furry and minty?

A polo bear

Why is a Christmas pudding

like the sea?

**They're both full
of currants**

What cereal do snowmen

have for breakfast?

Frosties

What sound does a turkey's phone make?

Wing wing, Wing wing

☆

What do Mexican snowmen most like to eat?

Brrrrr-itos

☆

How does Santa know who's been good at Christmas?

He asks the mince spies!

snow

laughing

matter

What often falls at the North Pole but never gets hurt?

Snow

Who is Frosty the Snowman's favourite aunt?

Aunt Artica

What goes, "Now you see me, now you don't?"

A snowman on a zebra crossing

Knock, knock!

Who's there?

Howard

Howard who?

Howard you like to stand out in the cold while some idiot keeps asking, **"Who's there?"**

What sort of ball doesn't bounce?
A snow ball

What do snowmen like to do in their free time?

Chill out

What did the snowman and his wife
hang over their baby's crib?

A snowmobile

Why is it so cold at Christmas?

**Because it's
Decembrrrrrr!**

How does a snowman
lose weight?

He sits in the sun

Knock, knock!

Who's there?

Atch

Atch who?

Bless you!

What do you call fifty penguins
in the Arctic?

Lost
(penguins live in Antarctica)

Where do snowmen go
to dance?

Snowballs!

What did the big furry hat
say to the warm woolly scarf?
**"You hang around while
I go on ahead"**

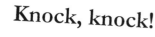

Knock, knock!

Who's there?

Icy

Icy who?

**Icy you standing
there in your nice
warm house!**

70

How do snowmen greet each

other for the first time?

It's ice to meet you

Why do adults always complain

in the Winter time?

**Because they're
GROAN-ups!**

What's Jack Frost's favourite

lesson in school?

Snow-and-tell

What do you get if you cross a snowman and a shark?

Frostbite

What's white and goes up but not down?

A confused snowflake

What did the snowman say to the annoying carrot?

"Get out of my face"

Knock, knock!

Who's there?

Scold

Scold who?

Scold outside, let me in!

What did the ocean say to the iceberg?

Nothing, it just waved

How do Eskimos make their beds?

With sheets of ice and blankets of snow

What do you call a gigantic
polar bear?

**Nothing, you just
run away!**

What's it called when a snowman
has a temper tantrum?

A meltdown

What did the snowman say
to the fallen leaf?

"You're so last season"

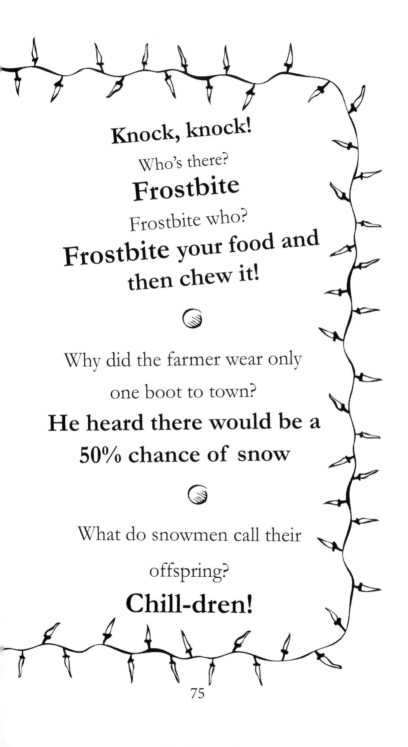

Knock, knock!

Who's there?

Frostbite

Frostbite who?

Frostbite your food and then chew it!

Why did the farmer wear only one boot to town?

He heard there would be a 50% chance of snow

What do snowmen call their offspring?

Chill-dren!

What happened when the snowgirl had a fight with the snowboy?

She gave him the cold shoulder

Knock, knock!

Who's there?

Snow

Snow who?

Snow use. I forgot my name again

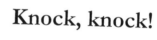

Why are there only snow men
and not snow women?

**Because girls are sensible
and know better than
to stand around in the cold
without a coat on**

What do you call an Eskimo cow?

An Eski̇moo

What do you call a snowman
on rollerskates?

A snowmobile

Why don't mountains get cold in the Winter?

They wear snow caps

Why do birds fly south in the Winter?

Because it's too far to walk!

How do snowmen get around?

By icicle

Knock, knock!

Who's there?

Emma

Emma who?

Emma bit cold out here,

let me in!

What do Eskimos use to hold
their houses together?

Ig-glue

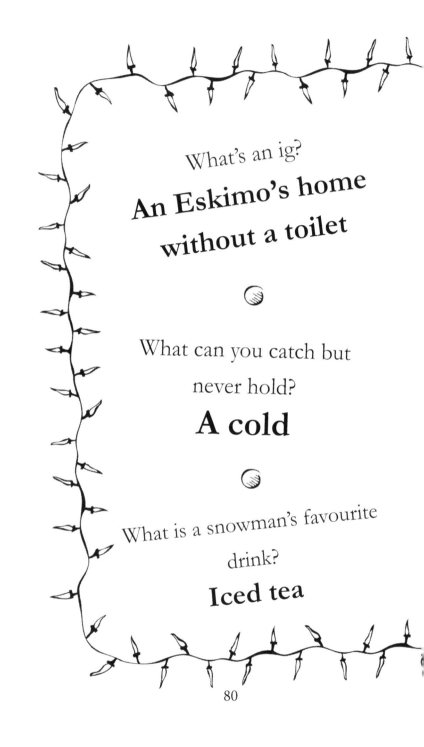

What's an ig?

An Eskimo's home without a toilet

What can you catch but never hold?

A cold

What is a snowman's favourite drink?

Iced tea

Knock, knock!

Who's there?

Snow

Snow who?

**Snowbody... Sorry to
disturb you!**

What did the policeman say to the
snowman when he caught
him stealing?

"Freeze!"

How do you scare a snowman?

**Point a hairdryer
at him**

Which one is faster, hot or cold?

Hot - you can catch a cold

☆

Knock, knock!

Who's there?

Lettuce

Lettuce who?

Lettuce in, it's snowing out here

☆

What do you call an old snowman?

A puddle

Pride and Partridges

(and other Christmas classics)

Much Ado About Stuffing

Green Eggnog and Ham

THE TAMING OF
THE SCROOGE

Of Mice and
Three Wise Men

YULEYSSES

CINDERELFA

LORD OF THE FIVE GOLDEN RINGS

Harry Potter and the
Chamber of Secret Santas

**Harry Potter and the
Prisoner of Marzipan**

FANTASTIC FEASTS AND
WHERE TO FIND THEM

PRIDE & PARTRIDGES

THE TURKEY WHO CAME TO TEA

Wrapunzel

THE THREE LITTLE
PIGS-IN-BLANKETS

The Princess and
the Brussels Sprout

JUST SNOW STORIES

86

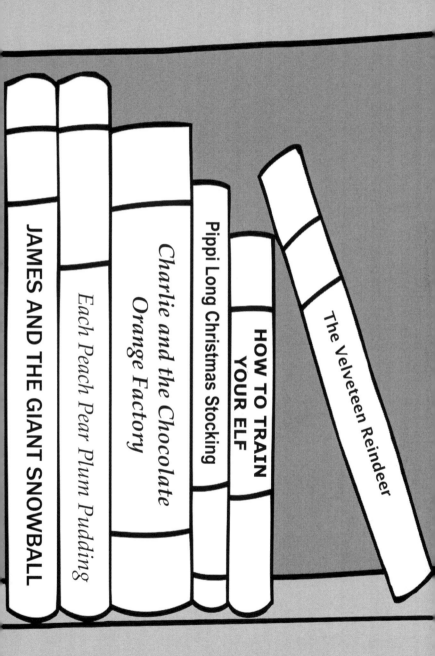

JAMES AND THE GIANT SNOWBALL

Each Peach Pear Plum Pudding

Charlie and the Chocolate Orange Factory

Pippi Long Christmas Stocking

HOW TO TRAIN YOUR ELF

The Velveteen Reindeer

FIVE GO CHRISTMAS CAROLING

LES MISTLETOE

We're Going On A
Polar Bear Hunt

THE JINGLE BOOK

THE SECRET
SANTA GARDEN

The Faraway
Christmas Tree

Where do the
Three Wise Men go to
get their robes tailored?

Bethle-hem

Knock, knock!

Who's there?

Honda

Honda who?

**Honda first day of
Christmas my true love sent
to me...**

Knock, knock!

Who's there?

Dexter

Dexter who?

Dexter halls with boughs of holly...

What Christmas carol do parents like best?

Silent Night!

What's Scrooge's favourite Christmas game?

Mean-opoly

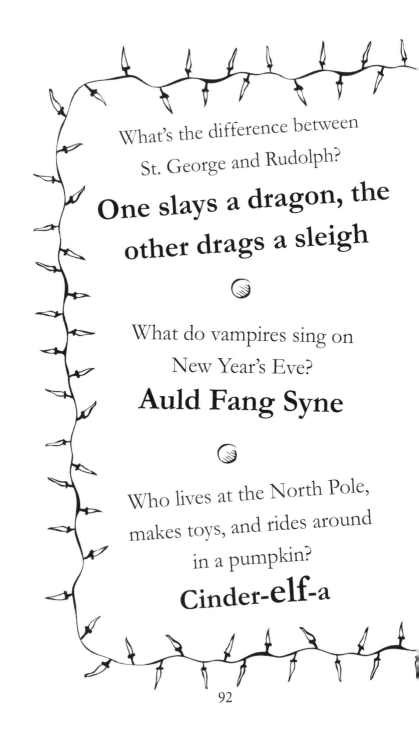

What's the difference between
St. George and Rudolph?

One slays a dragon, the other drags a sleigh

What do vampires sing on
New Year's Eve?

Auld Fang Syne

Who lives at the North Pole,
makes toys, and rides around
in a pumpkin?

Cinder-elf-a

Knock, knock!

Who's there?

Wenceslas

Wenceslas who?

Wenceslas train home?

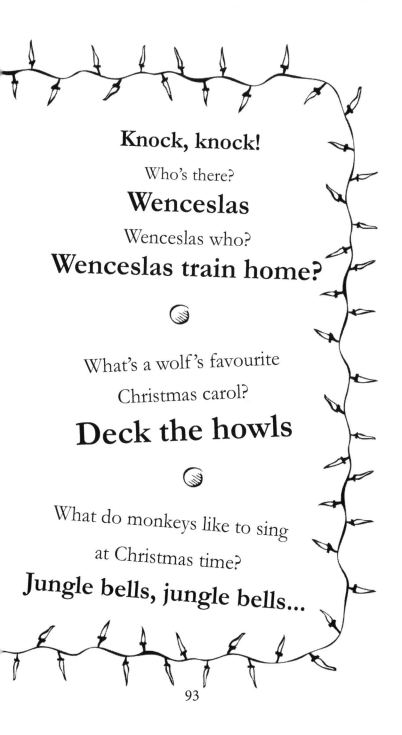

What's a wolf's favourite

Christmas carol?

Deck the howls

What do monkeys like to sing

at Christmas time?

Jungle bells, jungle bells...

What do you call a
Christmas tree with
a really big nose?
Pine-occhio

Knock, knock!

Who's there?

Oakham

Oakham who?

**Oakham All
Ye Faithful**

Knock, knock!

Who's there?

Tree

Tree who?

Tree wise men

What squeaks and only

appears in December?

The Ghost of

Christ-mouse Past

What's a dog's favourite

Christmas carol?

Bark, the Herald

Angels Sing

What's Santa's favourite pizza?

One that's deep pan, crisp and even

☆

Knock, knock!

Who's there?

Hannah

Hannah who?

Hannah partridge in a pear tree

☆

What Christmas carol do they sing in the desert?

Oh Camel Ye Faithful

Why did Santa's helper
see the doctor?

**Because he had
low elf esteem**

What illness do you get from eating
Christmas decorations?

Tinselitis

Knock, knock!

Who's there?

Pudding

Pudding who?

**Pudding up the
Christmas decorations**

Knock, knock!

Who's there?

Wanda

Wanda who?

Wanda know what
you're getting for Christmas?

What sort of music do
elves like best?

Wrap music!

Want to hear a joke about
wrapping paper?

Never mind, it's tear-able

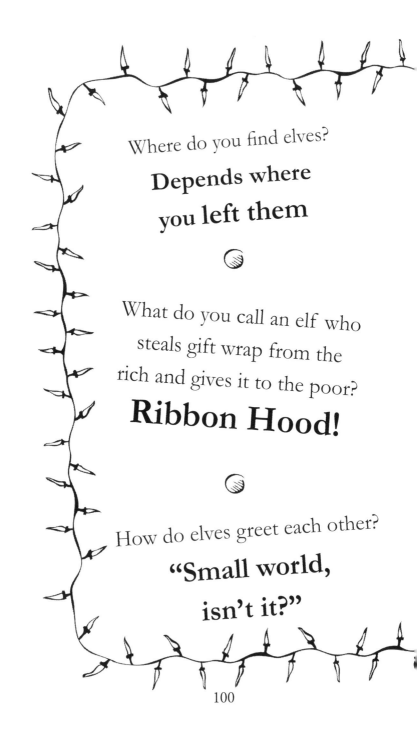

Where do you find elves?

Depends where you left them

What do you call an elf who steals gift wrap from the rich and gives it to the poor?

Ribbon Hood!

How do elves greet each other?

"Small world, isn't it?"

Knock, knock!

Who's there?

Donut

Donut who?

Donut open any presents before Christmas

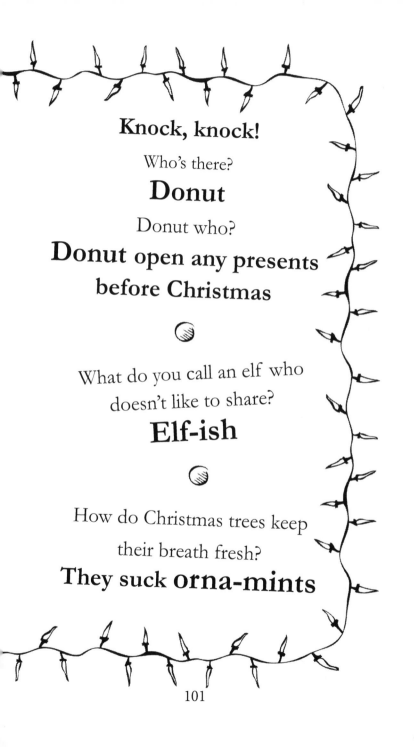

What do you call an elf who doesn't like to share?

Elf-ish

How do Christmas trees keep their breath fresh?

They suck orna-mints

Knock, knock!

Who's there?

Rabbit

Rabbit who?

Rabbit up carefully,
it's very fragile

Why do mummies like

Christmas so much?

Because of all the
wrapping

What kind of wreaths do

sea creatures like best?

Coral wreaths

What's green, covered in tinsel
and goes, "Ribbit, ribbit"?

Mistle-toad

What do caterpillars do
on New Year's Day?

Turn over a
new leaf

What's the best way
to decorate a boat at
Christmas time?

With oar-naments

What's a female elf called?

A shelf

☆

Knock, knock!

Who's there?

Asia

Asia who?

Asia time to take the Christmas tree down yet?

☆

How does Christmas Day end?

With the letter Y

ALSO AVAILABLE

If you enjoyed this book, you might also like Rudolph's Riddles, available from Amazon.

Rudolph's Riddles

OVER 200 RIDDLES HAND-PICKED BY RUDOLPH

Printed in Great Britain
by Amazon